The Very Dangerous Driver

TERENCE G. CROWTHER

READER
2A

OXFORD

UNIVERSITY PRESS

OXFORD
UNIVERSITY PRESS

198 Madison Avenue
New York, NY 10016 USA

Great Clarendon Street, Oxford OX2 6DP UK

Oxford University Press is a department of the
University of Oxford. It furthers the University's
objective of excellence in research, scholarship, and
education by publishing materials worldwide in

Oxford New York

Auckland Cape Town Dar es Salaam
Hong Kong Karachi Kuala Lumpur Madrid
Melbourne Mexico City Nairobi New Delhi
Shanghai Taipei Toronto

With offices in

Argentina Austria Brazil Chile Czech Republic
France Greece Guatemala Hungary Italy Japan
Poland Portugal Singapore South Korea
Switzerland Thailand Turkey Ukraine Vietnam

OXFORD and OXFORD ENGLISH are registered
trademarks of Oxford University Press

Executive Publisher: Nancy Leonhardt
Editorial Manager: Judith Cunningham
Editor: Kathryn L. O'Dell
Associate Editor: Carol Balistreri
Art Director: Lynn Luchetti
Design Project Manager: Amelia Carling
Designer: Jaclyn Smith
Layout Artist: Julie Macus
Art Editor: Judi DeSouter
Production Manager: Shanta Persaud
Production Controller: Eve Wong

ACKNOWLEDGMENTS

Design Studio: TWiNC/Color Associates Editorial and
Design Group, Inc.

ISBN: 978 019 440501 0

10 9 8 7 6 5 4 3

Printed in China

*This series is dedicated to Lucille Crowther, my late grandmother; to Frances Bernhardt, my surrogate
grandmother; and to Joshua, my son. Thanks for your faith, love, friendship, and encouragement.*
-T.G.C.

This is Jimmy Lee.
He is eleven years old.
He is funny. He is cool.
His radio is cool, too.

This is May Lee.
She is ten years old.
She is smart.
She is cute.
She is a good student.

This is Mr. Lee. He is a good father.
He is not a good driver.

Mr. Lee has a nice car.
His car is red.
It is fast.

"Come on, kids," says Mr. Lee.
"Let's go to the park.
Let's go in my car."

"No, thanks, Dad," says Jimmy.
"No, thanks, Dad," says May.

Mr. Lee is not happy.
"My car is nice!" he says.
"And it is fast! Come on."

Jimmy and May get in the car.
"Put on your seat belt,"
Jimmy says to May. They put on their
seat belts.

Mr. Lee drives. He is very happy.
"Look! A red bird!" he says.
"Look! A red light!" says Jimmy.

"A red light?" says Mr. Lee.
"What red light?"

"Oh, no!" say the children.

Mr. Lee drives. "Oh, no!" say the kids.
A blue bicycle stops.
A green scooter stops.
A pink car stops.
A yellow bus stops.
A red truck stops.

"Are you hungry, kids?" asks Mr. Lee.
"No," says Jimmy.

"Are you thirsty?" asks Mr. Lee.
"No," says May. "We are afraid."

"Why are you afraid?" asks Mr. Lee.
"Because you are not a good
driver, Dad," says Jimmy.

"I am a good driver," says Mr. Lee.
"Then look at the road sign!" says Jimmy.

"Road sign?" asks Mr. Lee.
"What road sign?"
"That one at the side of the road,"
says Jimmy.
"It means 'stop.'"
"Oh, no!" says May. "A train!"

The train stops. Mr. Lee stops, too.
"You are a bad driver," says the man
on the train.

Jimmy and May get out of the car. They stand next to it.

Mr. Lee is not happy.

"Get in the car, please," he says.

"No," says May. "We are afraid."

"You are a very good father," says Jimmy. "You are not a very good driver."

"I am a good driver," says Mr. Lee.
"No, you are not!" says the boy on the
blue bicycle.

"You are a bad driver," says the man on the green scooter.
The woman in the pink car looks at Jimmy and May. "That man is a dangerous driver," she says.

"He is a very dangerous driver," say the
bus driver and the truck driver.

A police officer stops. He is angry.
"What color is that light?" he asks.
"Light?" says Mr. Lee.
"What light?"

The police officer holds up three fingers.
"How many fingers?" he asks.
"I see two fingers," says Mr. Lee.

"Two fingers? No, three," says the
police officer.
"Your glasses are old. And you have very
bad eyes. Get new glasses, please."
"Yes, officer," says Mr. Lee.

"Now give me your car keys,"
says the police officer.
"OK," says Mr. Lee.

Mr. Lee is sad.
"It's OK, Dad," says Jimmy.
"Let's *walk* to the park."

"OK," says Mr. Lee. "Let's walk. I am not a very good driver."

"But you are a very good father," says May.

"Thank you," says Mr. Lee. "Now I am happy. Let's play."

New Words

Underline the new words in the sentences.

1 **funny**

This boy is <u>funny</u>.

2 **cool**

Jimmy is cool.

3 **kids**

"Jimmy and May are my kids," says Mr. Lee.

4 **Dad**

"This is my dad," says May. "Dad, this is Keri."

5 **seat belt**

May puts on the seat belt.

6 drive/drives

Mr. Lee drives the car
to the park.

7 Oh, no!

"Oh, no!" says May.

8 stop

"Stop," says the police
officer.

9 then

"I'm hungry," says May. "Then
eat an apple," says Mrs. Lee.

10 one

"This cat is Tabby. That
one is Sally," says May.

11 **mean/means**

A green light means "go."

12 **get out/gets out**

May gets out of the car.

13 **dangerous**

This driver is dangerous.

14 **glasses**

Mr. Lee puts on glasses.

15 **laugh**

Jimmy and May laugh.

Reading Comprehension

Circle the correct answer. Then write it in the blank.

1 How old is Jimmy?
He is __eleven__ years old.

ten   (eleven)

2 Jimmy's radio is _____.

red   cool

3 May is _____ and smart.

cute   cool

4 May is a good _____.

father   student

5 Mr. Lee is a _____ father.

good   bad

6 Mr. Lee has a new _____.

bicycle   car

Reading Comprehension

7 Mr. Lee's car is _____.

fast   slow

8 Mr. Lee says, "Let's go to the _____."

zoo   park

9 May and _____ put on their seat belts.

Mr. Lee   **Jimmy**

10 Mr. Lee sees a red _____.

bird   light

11 Are Jimmy and May hungry?
No, they are not. They are _____.

thirsty   afraid

12 Why are Jimmy and May afraid?
Because Mr. Lee is a _____ driver.

good   bad

13 The police officer is _____.

happy   **angry**

14 The police officer holds up _____ fingers.

two   **three**

15 Mr. Lee's eyes are _____.

bad   **good**

16 Why is Mr. Lee a dangerous driver? Because his glasses are _____.

new   **old**

17 The police officer says, "Now give me your _____."

glasses   **car keys**

18 Jimmy says, "Let's _____ to the park."

run   **walk**

Answer Key

1. eleven
2. cool
3. cute
4. student
5. good
6. car

7. fast
8. park
9. Jimmy
10. bird
11. afraid
12. bad

13. angry
14. three
15. bad
16. old
17. car keys
18. walk